STANDARD OF EXCELLENCE

ENHANCED COMPREHENSIVE BAND METHOD

By Bruce Pearson

Dear Student:

Welcome to the wonderful world of instrumental music. The moment you pick up your flute, you will begin an exciting adventure that is filled with challenges and rewards. If you study carefully and practice regularly, you will quickly discover the joy and satisfaction of playing beautiful music for yourself, your family, your friends, or a concert audience.

I hope you have many rewarding years of music-making.

Best wishes,

Bruce Pearson

Practice and Assessment - the key to EXCELLENCE!

▶ Make practicing part of your daily schedule. If you plan it as you do any other activity, you will find plenty of time for it.

▶ Try to practice in the same place every day. Choose a place where you can concentrate on making music. Start with a regular and familiar warm-up routine, including long tones and simple technical exercises. Like an athlete, you need to warm-up your mind and muscles before you begin performing.

▶ Always tune before you play. Use the tuning tracks found on the Accompaniment Recordings, or use the iPAS Tuner.

▶ Set goals for every practice session. Keep track of your practice time and progress on the front cover Practice Journal.

▶ Practice the difficult spots in your lesson assignment and band music over and over at a slower tempo, until you can play them perfectly, then gradually increase the tempo. Use the iPAS Metronome to track your progress and ensure you are playing with a steady pulse.

▶ Spend time practicing alone and with the Accompaniment Recordings.

▶ Assess your progress and achievements by using iPAS. Listen to the recordings you create to hear the spots in the music which might need improvement.

▶ At the end of each practice session, play something fun!

ISBN 0-8497-0750-1

kjos NEIL A. KJOS MUSIC COMPANY, PUBLISHER

PUTTING YOUR FLUTE TOGETHER

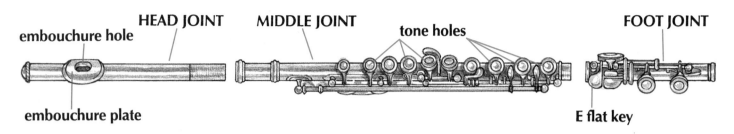

embouchure hole   **HEAD JOINT**   **MIDDLE JOINT**   **tone holes**   **FOOT JOINT**

embouchure plate   **E flat key**

STEP 1
Open your case right side up.

STEP 2
Put the head joint into the middle joint with a gentle twisting motion.

STEP 3
Line up the embouchure hole with the center of the tone holes.

STEP 4
Hold the assembled head and middle joints and gently twist on the foot joint.

STEP 5
Line up the foot joint so the rod is centered with the tone holes.

PREPARING TO PLAY

STEP 1
Sit up straight on the edge of your chair.

STEP 2
Make a "C" with your left hand so that you form a shelf at the base of your thumb. Rest the flute on that shelf.

STEP 3
Place your left thumb on the long straight key on the underside of the flute. Move your left hand to the right and rest the flute at the base of the index finger between the knuckle and first joint.

STEP 4
Place the tip of your right thumb under the flute between the first and second fingers.

STEP 5
Curving your fingers on both hands, place your right little finger on the Eb key. Your elbows should be away from your body. The flute should be pointing slightly downward.

CARING FOR YOUR FLUTE

STEP 1
After playing, dry the inside of your flute with a soft cloth over a cleaning rod.

STEP 2
Shake the water out of the head joint. Wipe the joints clean.

STEP 3
Wipe the outside of your flute with a soft, clean cloth. Carefully put away all parts of your flute and latch your case.

PLAYING YOUR FLUTE

STEP 1
Remove the head joint and place your right hand over the open end. Shape your mouth as if saying "whee-too."

STEP 2
Place the head joint on your chin, and position it so that the edge of the embouchure hole is at the bottom of the lower lip. The corners of the lower lip should rest against the embouchure plate.

STEP 3
Cover 1/4 to 1/3 of the embouchure hole with your lower lip. Take a full breath of air and blow over the hole using the syllable "doo" to play a long, steady tone.

STEP 4
Assemble the head joint to the body. Position your flute to the right of your body, with the flute pointing slightly downward.

STEP 5
Take a full breath of air and play a long, steady tone.

FOR FLUTES ONLY

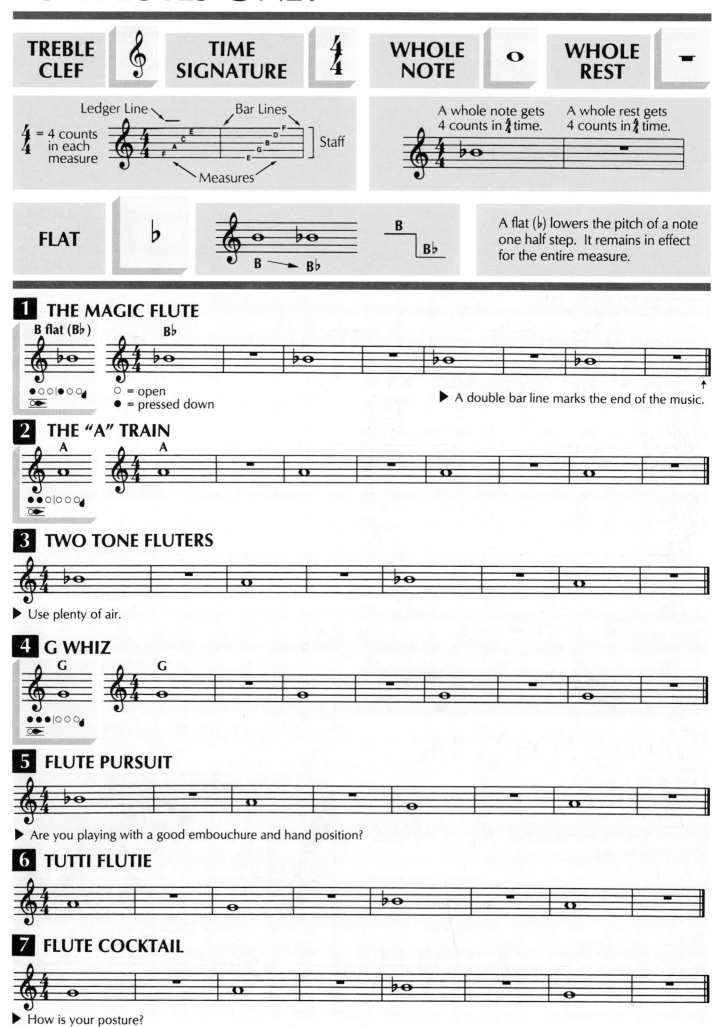

TREBLE CLEF | **TIME SIGNATURE** 4/4 | **WHOLE NOTE** o | **WHOLE REST** —

4/4 = 4 counts in each measure

Ledger Line — Bar Lines — Staff — Measures

A whole note gets 4 counts in 4/4 time.   A whole rest gets 4 counts in 4/4 time.

FLAT ♭

B → B♭   B / B♭

A flat (♭) lowers the pitch of a note one half step. It remains in effect for the entire measure.

1 THE MAGIC FLUTE

B flat (B♭)   B♭

○ = open
● = pressed down

▶ A double bar line marks the end of the music.

2 THE "A" TRAIN

A   A

3 TWO TONE FLUTERS

▶ Use plenty of air.

4 G WHIZ

G   G

5 FLUTE PURSUIT

▶ Are you playing with a good embouchure and hand position?

6 TUTTI FLUTIE

7 FLUTE COCKTAIL

▶ How is your posture?

FOR WOODWINDS ONLY

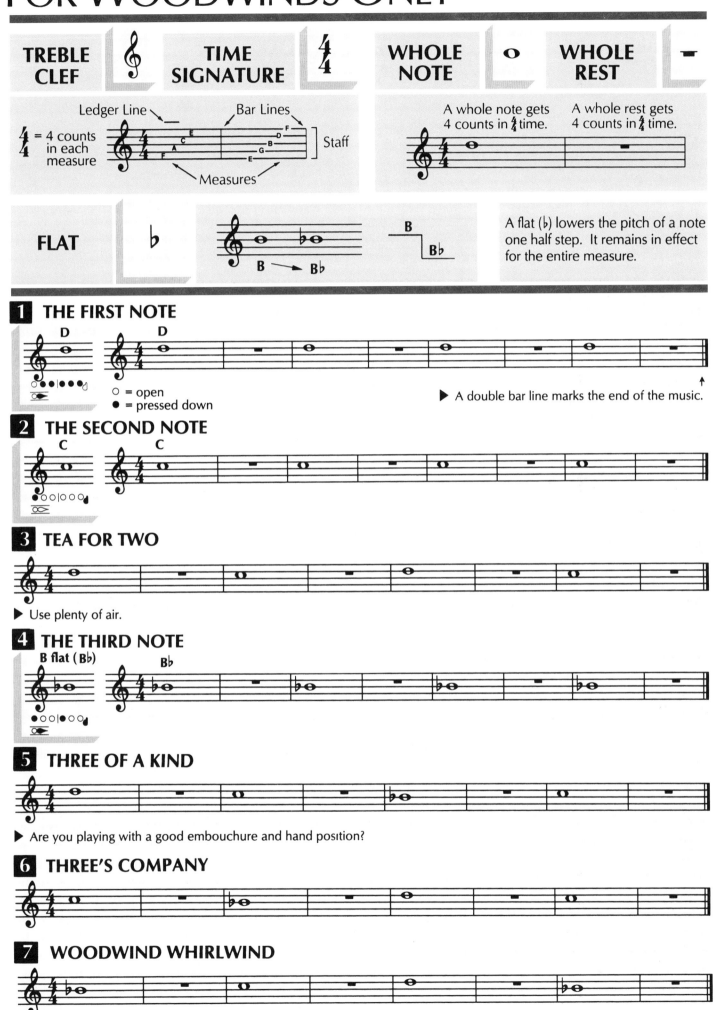

FOR THE FULL BAND

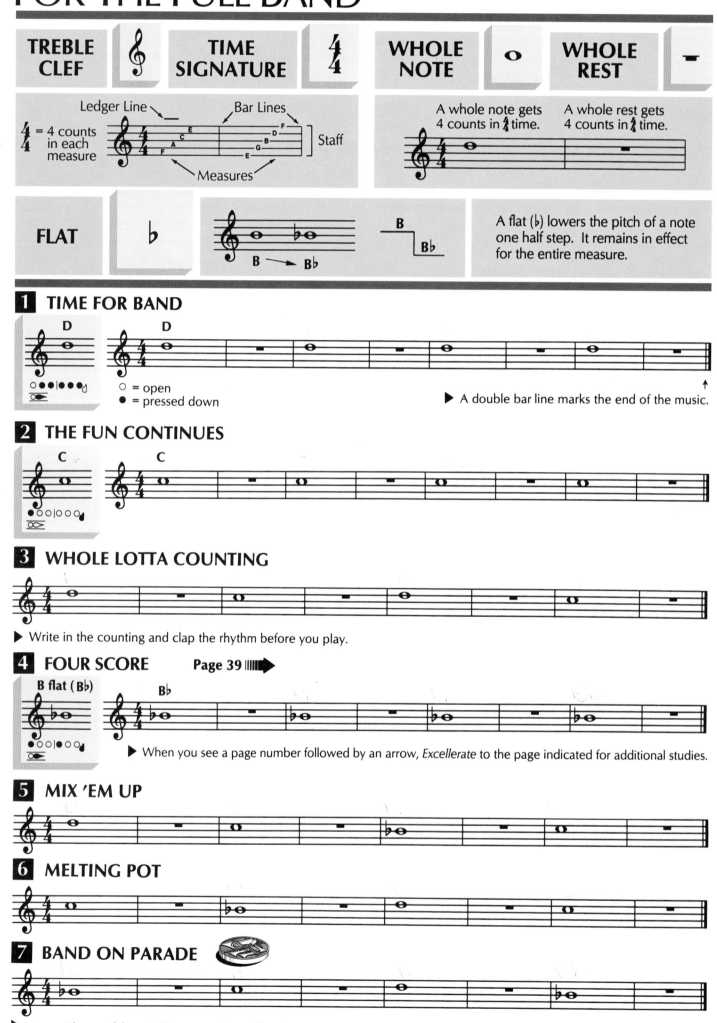

Star Spangled Banner

Arr. by Keith Pennings & Jean Narunsky

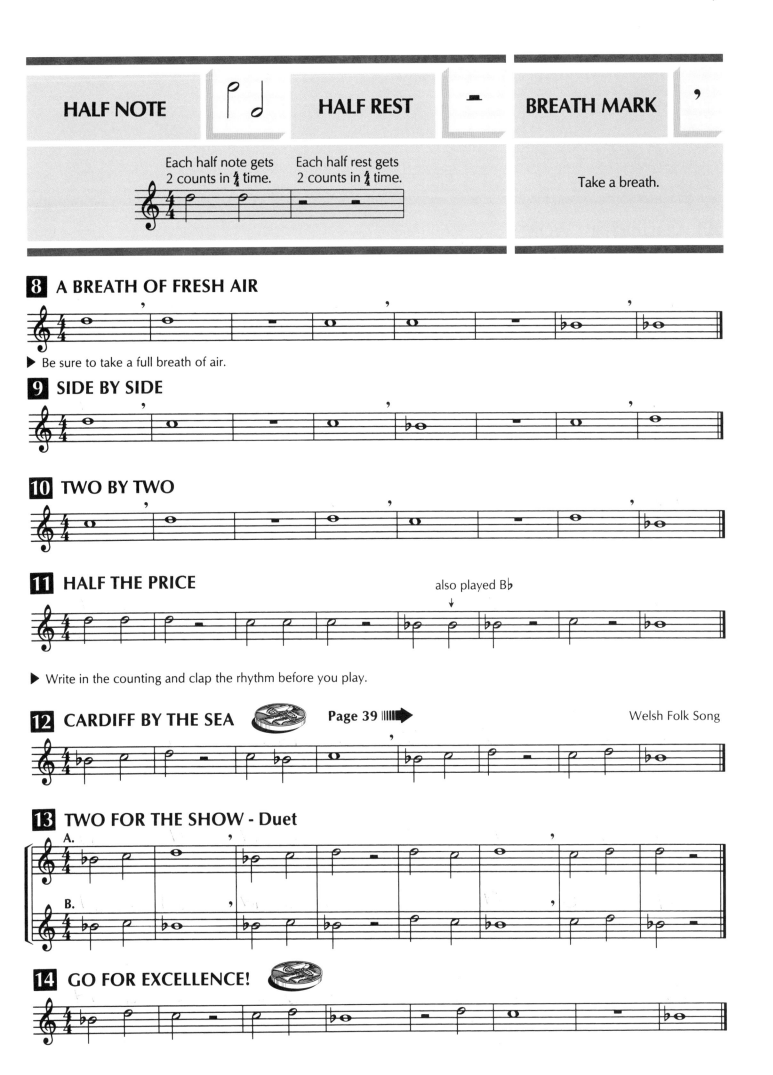

HALF NOTE | HALF REST | BREATH MARK

Each half note gets 2 counts in ₄₄ time.

Each half rest gets 2 counts in ₄₄ time.

Take a breath.

8 A BREATH OF FRESH AIR

▶ Be sure to take a full breath of air.

9 SIDE BY SIDE

10 TWO BY TWO

11 HALF THE PRICE

also played B♭

▶ Write in the counting and clap the rhythm before you play.

12 CARDIFF BY THE SEA   Page 39   Welsh Folk Song

13 TWO FOR THE SHOW - Duet

A.

B.

14 GO FOR EXCELLENCE!

PW21FL

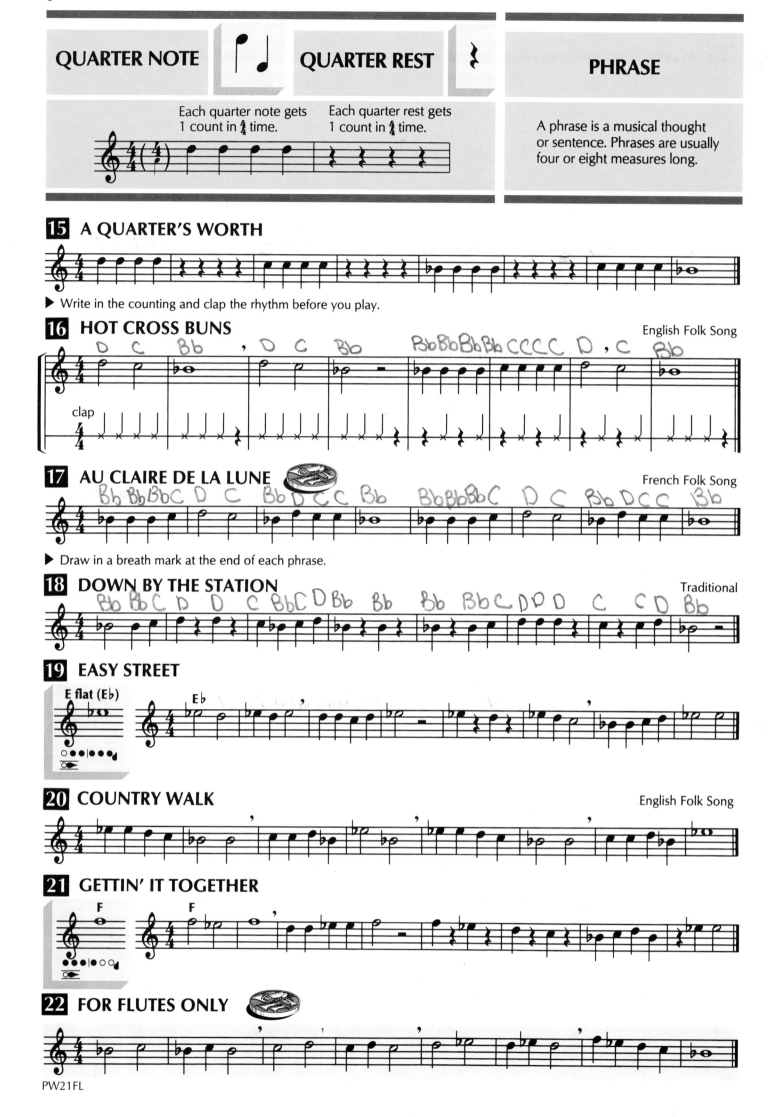

REPEAT SIGN	COMMON TIME	FERMATA	SOLO	One person plays.
	C	⌢•	SOLI	Whole section plays.
Repeat from the beginning.	**C** = 4/4 Common time means the same as 4/4 time.	Hold the note or rest longer than its usual value.	TUTTI	Everyone plays.

23 MERRILY WE ROLL ALONG   Page 39   Traditional

DC BbC DD D, C C C   D F F   DC Bb C DDD, C CD C Bb

▶ Write in the note names before you play.

24 LIGHTLY ROW - Duet   Traditional

25 ONE STEP AT A TIME

▶ Write in the counting and clap the rhythm before you play.

26 GOOD KING WENCESLAS   Traditional English Carol

Solo/Soli Eb F   Eb Eb Bb   Tutti Bb C D Eb Eb,   Solo/Soli Eb F Eb Eb Eb   Bb   Tutti Bb C D Eb Eb

27 SONG OF THE FJORDS   Norwegian Folk Song

Solo/Soli   , Tutti   Solo/Soli   , Tutti

28 _____   Composer _____
                                                              your name

▶ Fill in the rest of the measures using the given rhythms and any notes you know. Title and play your composition.

29 GO FOR EXCELLENCE!   ✓

PW21FL

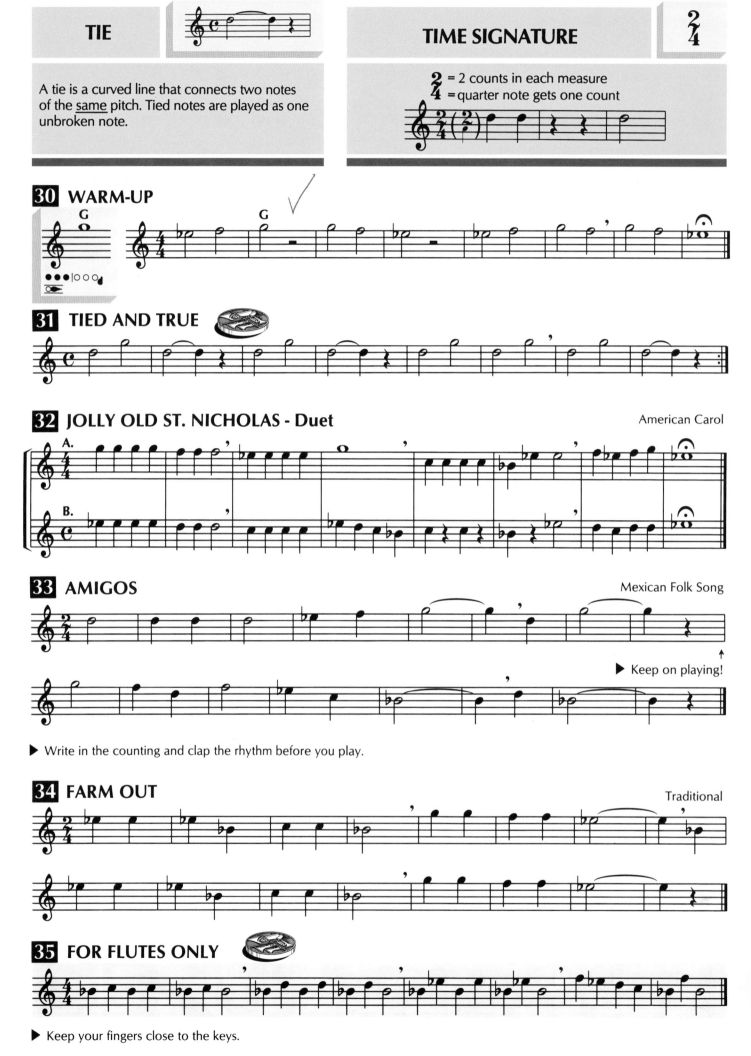

TIE

A tie is a curved line that connects two notes of the <u>same</u> pitch. Tied notes are played as one unbroken note.

TIME SIGNATURE

$\frac{2}{4}$

$\frac{2}{4}$ = 2 counts in each measure
$\frac{2}{4}$ = quarter note gets one count

30 WARM-UP

31 TIED AND TRUE

32 JOLLY OLD ST. NICHOLAS - Duet

American Carol

33 AMIGOS

Mexican Folk Song

▶ Keep on playing!

▶ Write in the counting and clap the rhythm before you play.

34 FARM OUT

Traditional

35 FOR FLUTES ONLY

▶ Keep your fingers close to the keys.

KEY SIGNATURE

Key signatures change certain notes throughout a piece of music. This key signature means play all B's as B flats and all E's as E flats.

36 MARK TIME

▶ For lower notes, make your lip opening larger and direct your air stream lower.

37 SWEETLY SINGS THE DONKEY - Round

Traditional

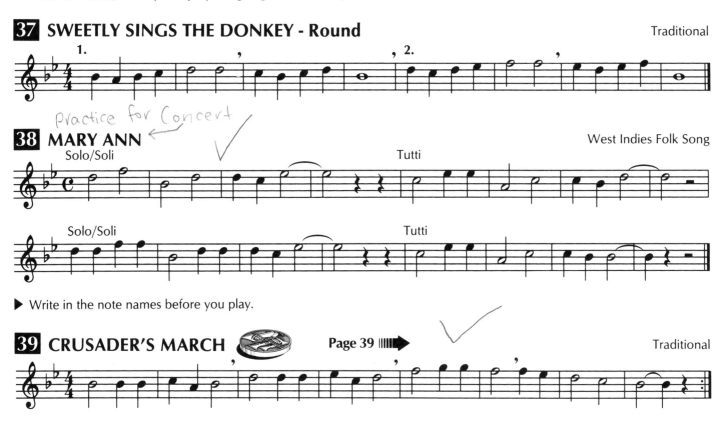

Practice for Concert

38 MARY ANN

West Indies Folk Song

Solo/Soli   Tutti

Solo/Soli   Tutti

▶ Write in the note names before you play.

39 CRUSADER'S MARCH

Page 39

Traditional

▶ Write in the counting and clap the rhythm before you play.

40 BALANCE THE SCALES

Draw *one* note or *one* rest to balance each scale.

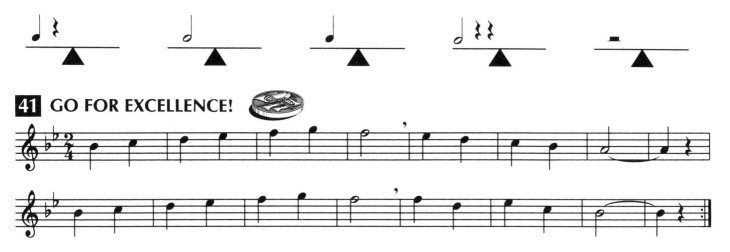

41 GO FOR EXCELLENCE!

| **DIVISI** | Part of the section plays the top notes and part of the section plays the bottom notes. |  |
| **UNISON** | Everyone plays the same notes. | |

BALANCE BUILDER

JINGLE BELLS
Band Arrangement

J. S. Pierpont (1822 - 1893)
arr. Chuck Elledge (b. 1961)

42 **SCHOOL SONG**

43 **FOR FLUTES ONLY**

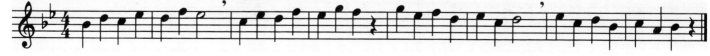

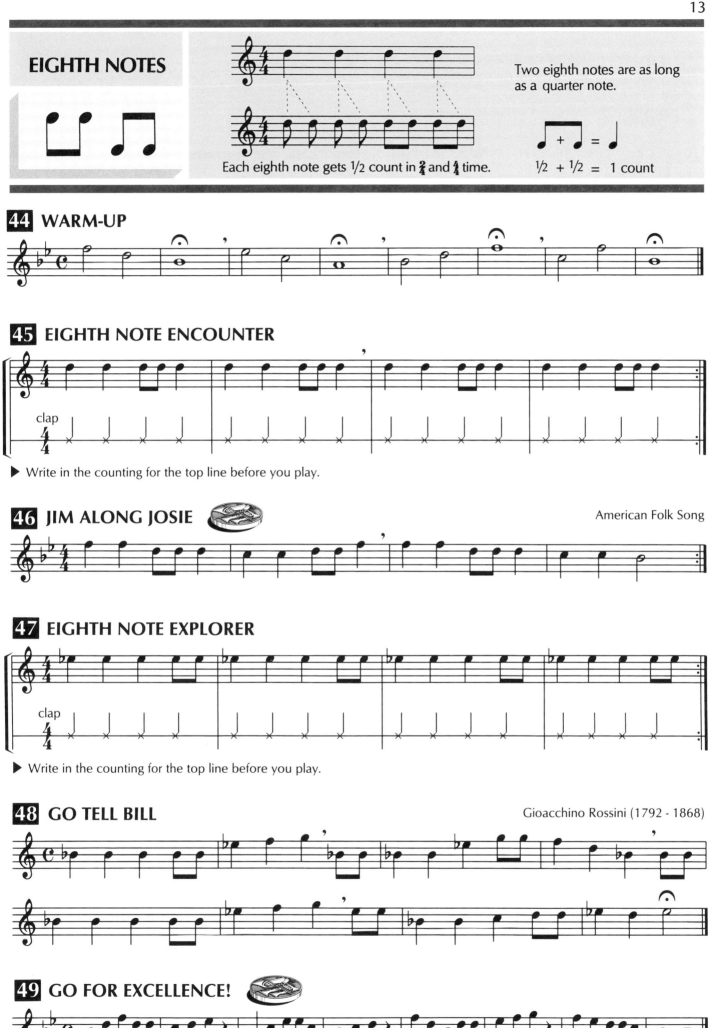

14

50 EIGHTH NOTE EXPRESS

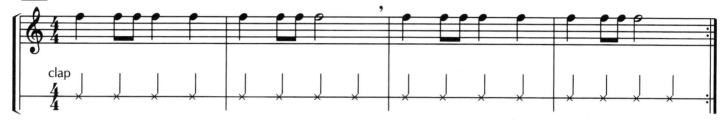

▶ Write in the counting for the top line before you play.

51 SKIP IT, LOU

American Folk Song

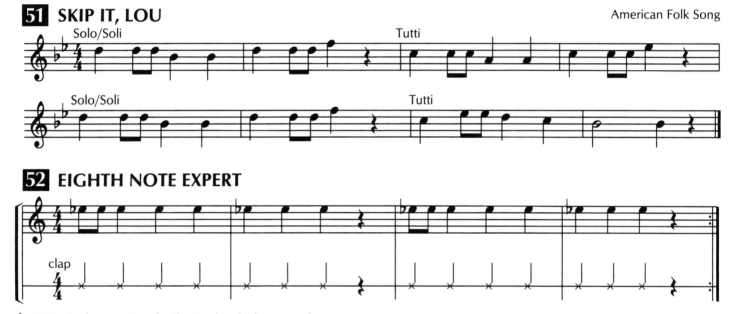

52 EIGHTH NOTE EXPERT

▶ Write in the counting for the top line before you play.

53 MEXICAN MOUNTAIN SONG

Mexican Folk Song

54 BAFFLING BAR LINES

▶ Write in the counting and draw in the bar lines before you play.

55 FOR FLUTES ONLY

▶ For higher notes, make your lip opening smaller and direct your air stream higher.

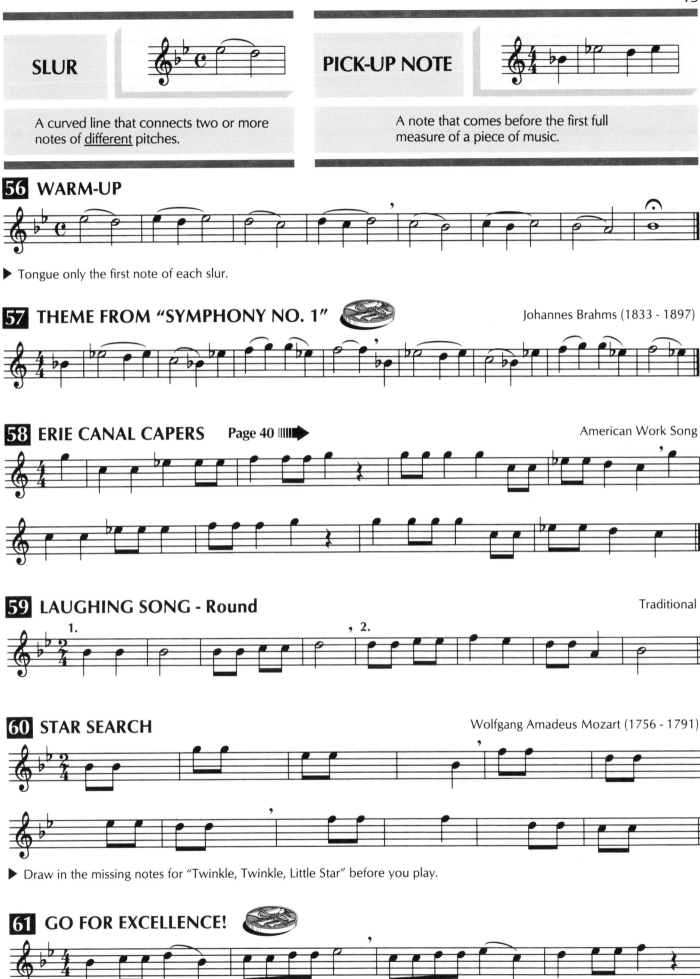

SLUR

A curved line that connects two or more notes of different pitches.

PICK-UP NOTE

A note that comes before the first full measure of a piece of music.

56 WARM-UP

▶ Tongue only the first note of each slur.

57 THEME FROM "SYMPHONY NO. 1"

Johannes Brahms (1833 - 1897)

58 ERIE CANAL CAPERS Page 40

American Work Song

59 LAUGHING SONG - Round

Traditional

60 STAR SEARCH

Wolfgang Amadeus Mozart (1756 - 1791)

▶ Draw in the missing notes for "Twinkle, Twinkle, Little Star" before you play.

61 GO FOR EXCELLENCE!

PW21FL

 **KEY SIGNATURE**

This key signature means play all B's as B flats, all E's as E flats, and all A's as A flats.

62 CLIMBING STAIRS

63 BINGO American Folk Song

64 THERE'S MUSIC IN THE AIR George F. Root (1820 - 1895)

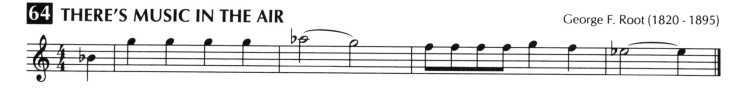

65 THERE'S THE SAME MUSIC IN THE AIR George F. Root (1820 - 1895)

▶ Circle the notes changed by the key signature.

66 SCALE SKILL

67 FOR FLUTES ONLY

DOTTED HALF NOTE

A dot after a note adds half the value of the note.

♩ + • = ♩ + ♩ = ♩.
2 + 1 = 2 + 1 = 3 counts

TIME SIGNATURE

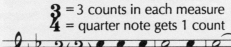
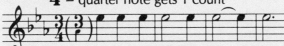

3 = 3 counts in each measure
4 = quarter note gets 1 count

DYNAMICS

forte (*f*) - loud
piano (*p*) - soft

68 WARM-UP

69 CHANNEL THREE

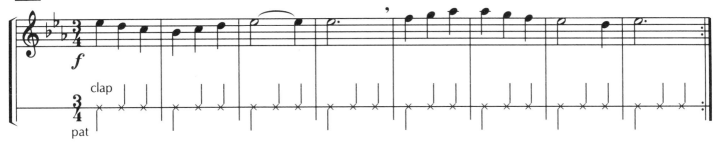

▶ Write in the counting for the top line before you play.

70 DOWN IN THE VALLEY American Mountain Song

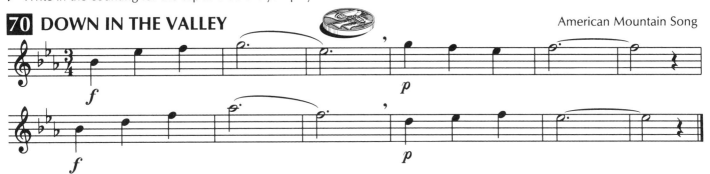

71 BROTHER MARTIN - Round Latin American Folk Song

72 THE LITTLE FISH Australian Folk Song

▶ Draw in a breath mark at the end of each phrase.

73 GO FOR EXCELLENCE! Czech Folk Song
"When Love Is Kind"

PW21FL

18

NATURAL

A natural sign cancels a flat or a sharp.
It remains in effect for the entire measure.

74 WARM-UP

75 OLD BLUE — Traditional

76 THIRD TIME AROUND

▶ Circle the notes changed by the key signature.

77 LULLABY - Duet — Traditional

78 MINUTEMAN MARCH — Robert Frost (b. 1942)

also played A♮

79 FOR FLUTES ONLY

PW21FL

The written piano accompaniment for SAWMILL CREEK is included on track 1 of CD 2 for easy access in a performance situation.

SAWMILL CREEK
Solo with Piano Accompaniment

Bruce Pearson (b. 1942)

▶ Go back to the first repeat sign.

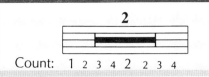

LONG REST — Rest the number of measures indicated.

85 WARM-UP

▶ Move your lower jaw and lips back for lower notes.

86 FULL OF HOT AIR

87 DANZA GIOVANNI

Italian Folk Song

88 B♭ MAJOR SCALE SKILL   Page 40

Arpeggio

Chords
div.

89 THE MAN ON THE FLYING TRAPEZE

George Leybourne (1842 - 1884)

1.   2.

▶ Go back to the first repeat sign.

90 _____   Composer _____
                                                              your name

▶ Using the given rhythms, draw in notes to complete the melody. Title and play your composition.

91 FOR FLUTES ONLY

92 LOOK SHARP

93 AURA LEE

G. R. Poulton (d. 1867)

94 BARCAROLLE

Jacques Offenbach (1819 - 1880)

95 JUST BY ACCIDENT

96 F MAJOR SCALE SKILL

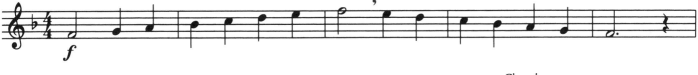

97 SAILOR'S SONG

▶ For lower notes, make your lip opening larger and direct your air stream lower.

98 GO FOR EXCELLENCE!

"This Old Man"

American Folk Song

PW21FL

DA CAPO AL FINE (D. C. AL FINE)

Go back to the beginning and play until the *Fine*.

SHARP

A sharp (♯) raises the pitch of a note one half step.
It remains in effect for the entire measure.

99 WARM-UP

100 IN THE POCKET

101 POCKET CHANGE

102 STRICTLY BUSINESS

103 SMOOTH SAILING

104 ROSES FROM THE SOUTH

Johann Strauss, Jr. (1825 - 1899)

105 THEME FROM "HANSEL AND GRETEL"

Engelbert Humperdinck (1854 - 1921)

106 FOR FLUTES ONLY

Page 40 ▶

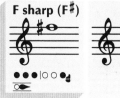

107 THAT'S A WRAP

108 POLLY WOLLY DOODLE   American Folk Song

clap

foot stomp

109 VOLGA BOAT SONG   Russian Folk Song

110   Composer _____
                                                                                    your name
Hand Clappers

Knee Slappers

▶ Compose a duet (accompaniment) part for Knee Slappers. The first measure has been completed for you. Title and perform your composition.

111 GO FOR EXCELLENCE!   Tielman Susato (1500? - 1561?)

"Ronde"

| SINGLE EIGHTH NOTE | | A single eighth note is half as long as a quarter note. ♪ = ½ count |
| DOTTED QUARTER NOTE |  | A dot after a note adds half the value of the note. ♩ + • = ♩ + ♪ = ♩. 1 + ½ = 1 + ½ = 1 ½ counts |

112 WARM-UP - Band Arrangement

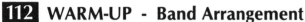

113 SHORT CUT

▶ Write in the counting for the top line before you play.

114 SPOT THE DOTS

▶ Feel the pulse of three eighth notes during each dotted quarter note.

115 ALL THROUGH THE NIGHT

Welsh Folk Song

116 ALOUETTE

French-Canadian Folk Song
Fine

D.C. al Fine

117 FOR FLUTES ONLY

PW21FL

118 JUST A LITTLE OFF THE TOP

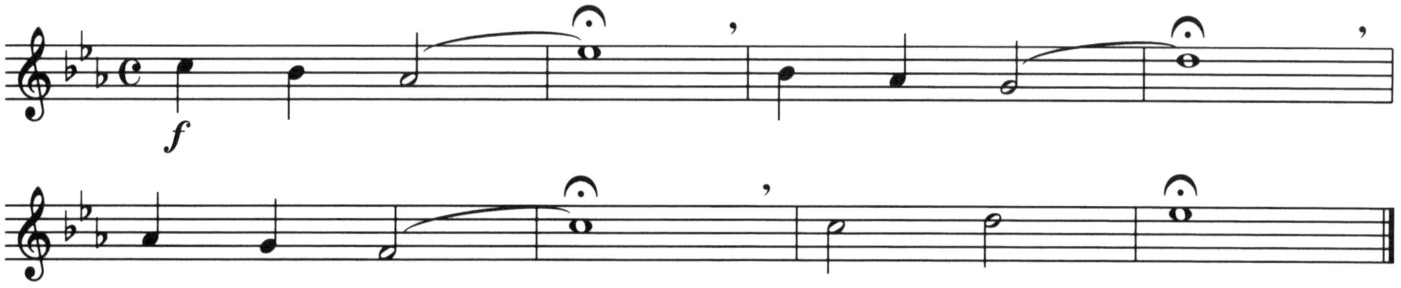

▶ For higher notes, make your lip opening smaller and direct your air stream higher.

119 TOP DRAWER - Duet

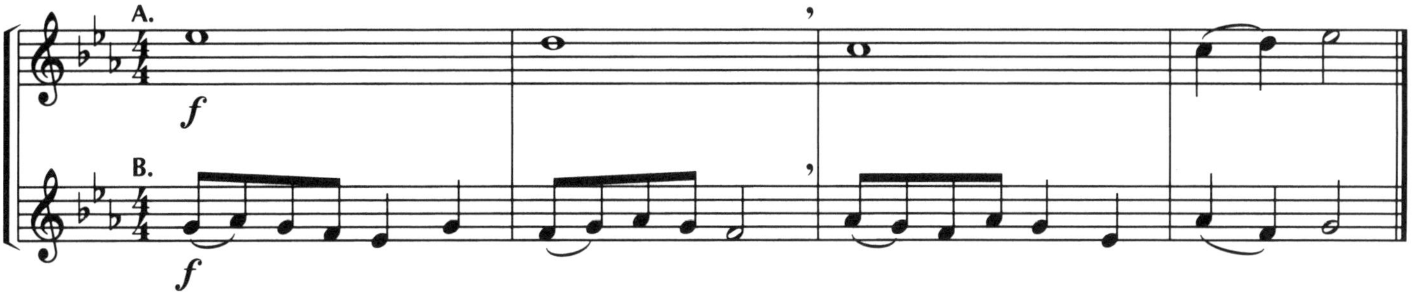

120 HOME ON THE RANGE Page 41

Daniel E. Kelley (1843 - 1905)

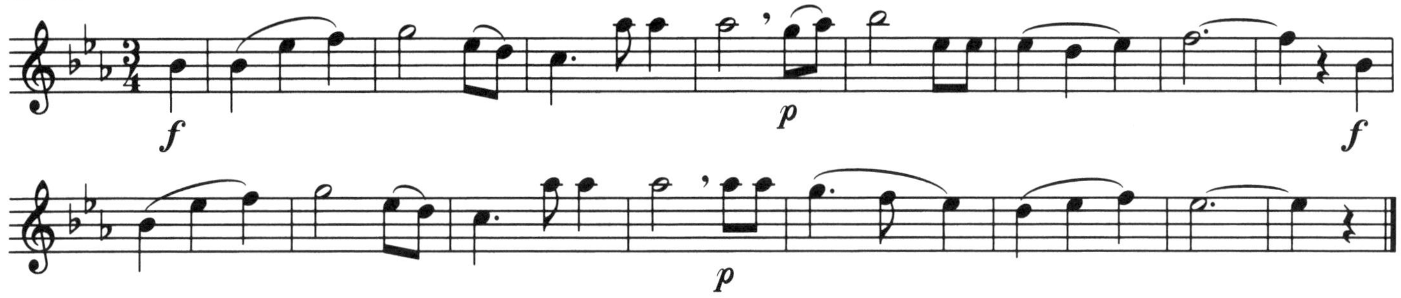

▶ Circle the notes changed by the key signature.

121 THE CONQUERING HERO - Duet

George Frideric Handel (1685 - 1759)

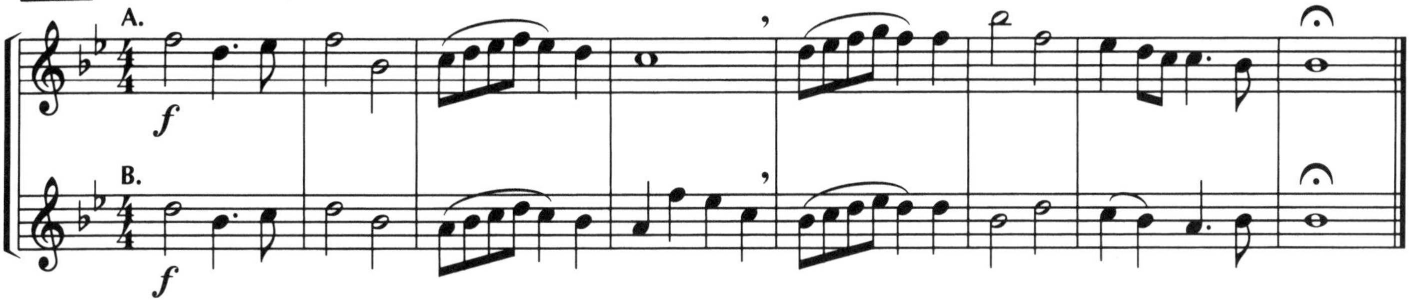

122 GO FOR EXCELLENCE!

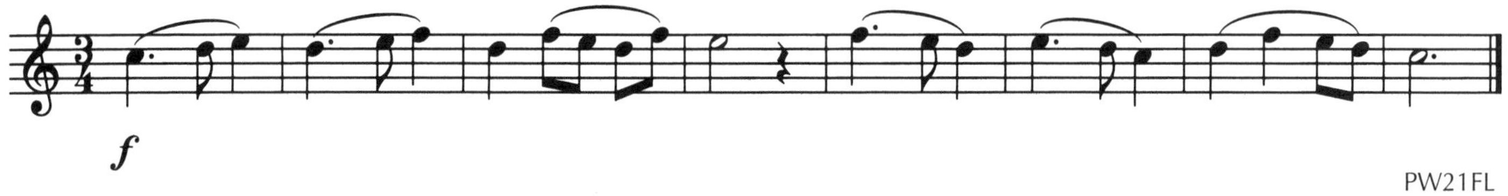

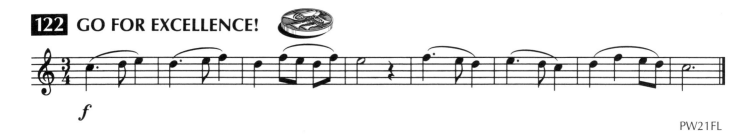

| TEMPOS | **Andante** - moderately slow
Moderato - moderate speed
Allegro - quick and lively | DYNAMICS | *mezzo forte* (**mf**) - medium loud
mezzo piano (**mp**) - medium soft |

123 WARM-UP - Band Arrangement

124 HIGH WINDS AHEAD

125 LOOK BEFORE YOU LEAP

126 E♭ MAJOR SCALE SKILL

127 VARIATIONS ON A THEME BY MOZART

Wolfgang Amadeus Mozart (1756 – 1791)

128 FOR FLUTES ONLY

▶ For higher notes, make your lip opening smaller and direct your air stream higher.

BALANCE BUILDER

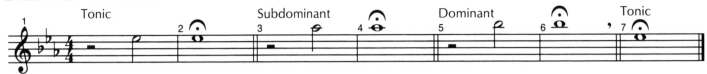

TRUMPET VOLUNTARY
Band Arrangement

Jeremiah Clarke (1674? - 1707)
arr. Bruce Pearson (b. 1942)

TEMPO	*Ritardando (**ritard.** or **rit.**)* - Gradually slow the tempo.

135 SAKURA - Duet

Andante

Japanese Folk Song

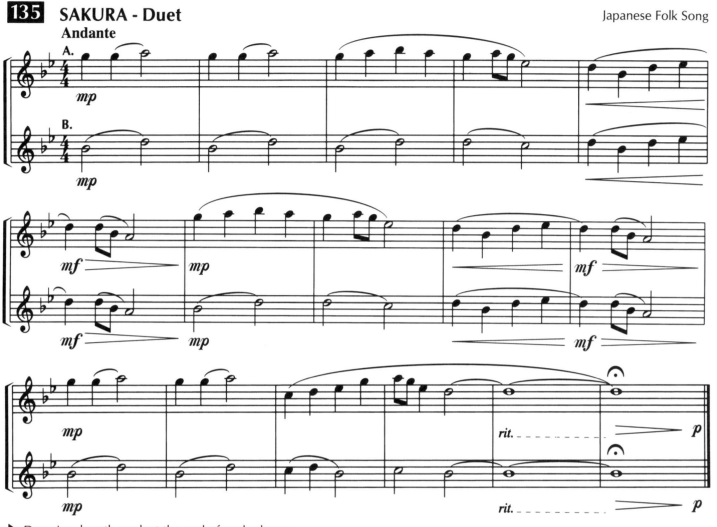

▶ Draw in a breath mark at the end of each phrase.

136 GRANDFATHER'S WHISKERS

Moderato

American Folk Song

Hey!

137 TWINKLE VARIATION

Wolfgang Amadeus Mozart (1756 – 1791)

Theme

Composer _____

your name

Variation

▶ Compose a variation on "Twinkle, Twinkle, Little Star."

PW21FL

140 DYNAMIC DECISION

Write in the following dynamics from softest to loudest: *mezzo forte*   *piano*   *forte*   *mezzo piano*

softest ⟵──────────────────────────────⟶ loudest

147 RICOCHET ROCK

Chuck Elledge (b. 1961)

Allegro

148 LOCH LOMOND

Scottish Folk Song

Moderato

149 SHALOM, CHAVERIM

Hebrew Folk Song

Andante

▶ Draw in a breath mark at the end of each phrase.

150 _____ Composer _____

your name

▶ Compose an ending for this melody. Title and play your composition.

151 FOR FLUTES ONLY

Moderato

▶ Move your lower jaw and lips forward for higher tones and backward for lower tones.

152 GRANDFATHER'S CLOCK — Henry C. Work (1832 - 1884)

▶ Circle the note changed by the key signature.

153 KUM BA YAH — African Folk Song

154 GRANT US PEACE - Round — German Canon

155 GO FOR EXCELLENCE!

MINUET

Solo with Piano Accompaniment

Johann Sebastian Bach
(1685 – 1750)

ROCKIN' RONDEAU
Band Arrangement

Based on a theme by
Jean-Joseph Mouret (1682 – 1738)
arr. Chuck Elledge (b. 1961)

EXCELLERATORS-For Flutes Only

TIE

A tie is a curved line that connects two notes of the <u>same</u> pitch. Tied notes are played as one unbroken note.

SLUR

A slur is a curved line that connects two or more notes of <u>different</u> pitches. Tongue only the first note of a slur.

EXCELLERATORS- For Flutes Only

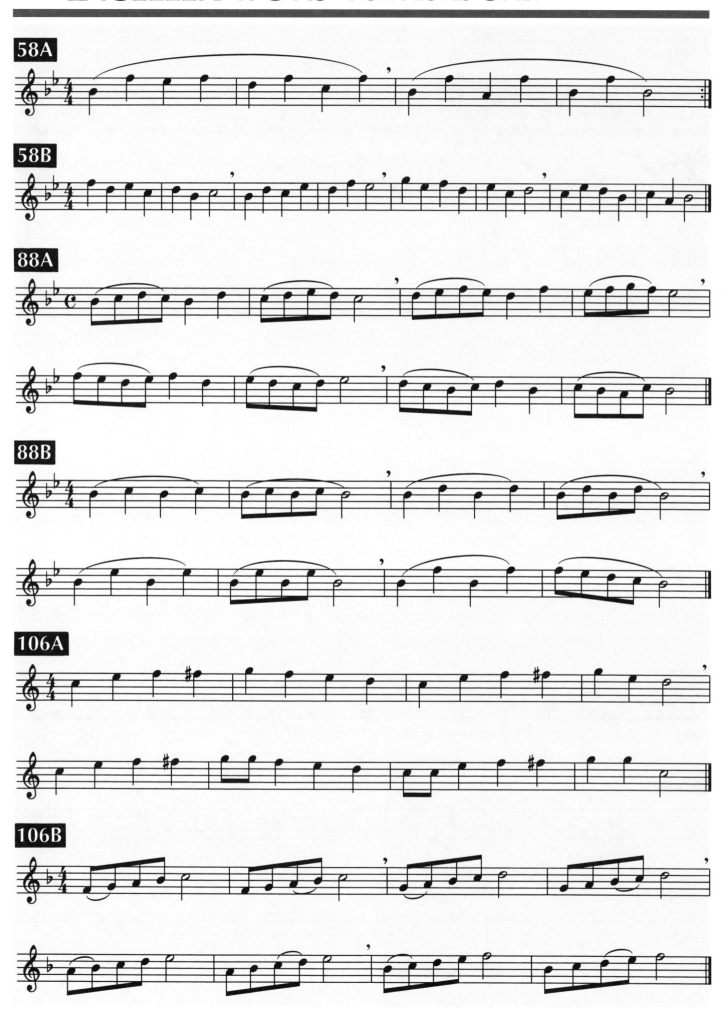

EXCELLERATORS-FOR FLUTES ONLY

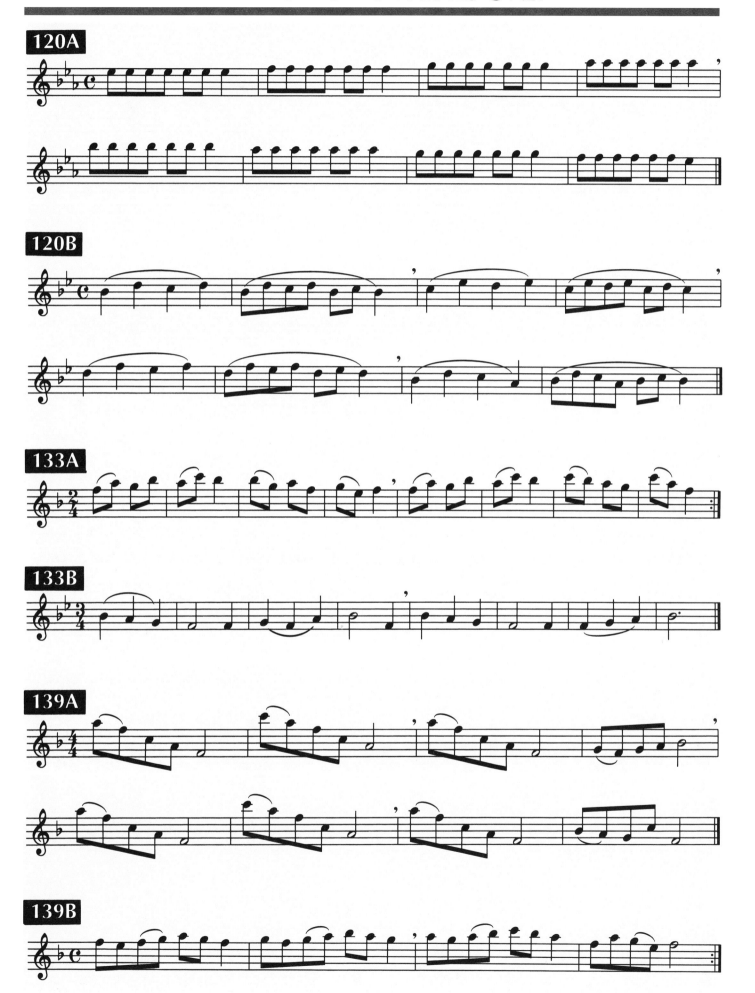

SCALE STUDIES

B♭ MAJOR SCALE

Arpeggio

Thirds

E♭ MAJOR SCALE

Arpeggio

Thirds

F MAJOR SCALE

Arpeggio

Thirds

A♭ MAJOR SCALE

Arpeggio

Thirds

CHROMATIC SCALE

RHYTHM STUDIES

$\frac{4}{4}$ or **C**

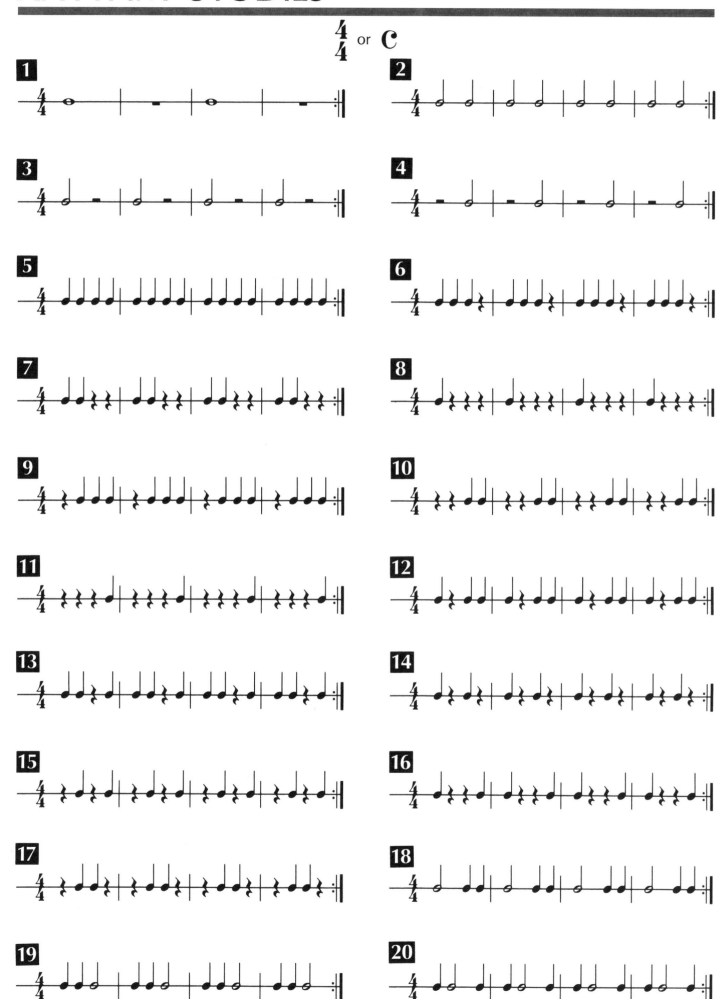

RHYTHM STUDIES

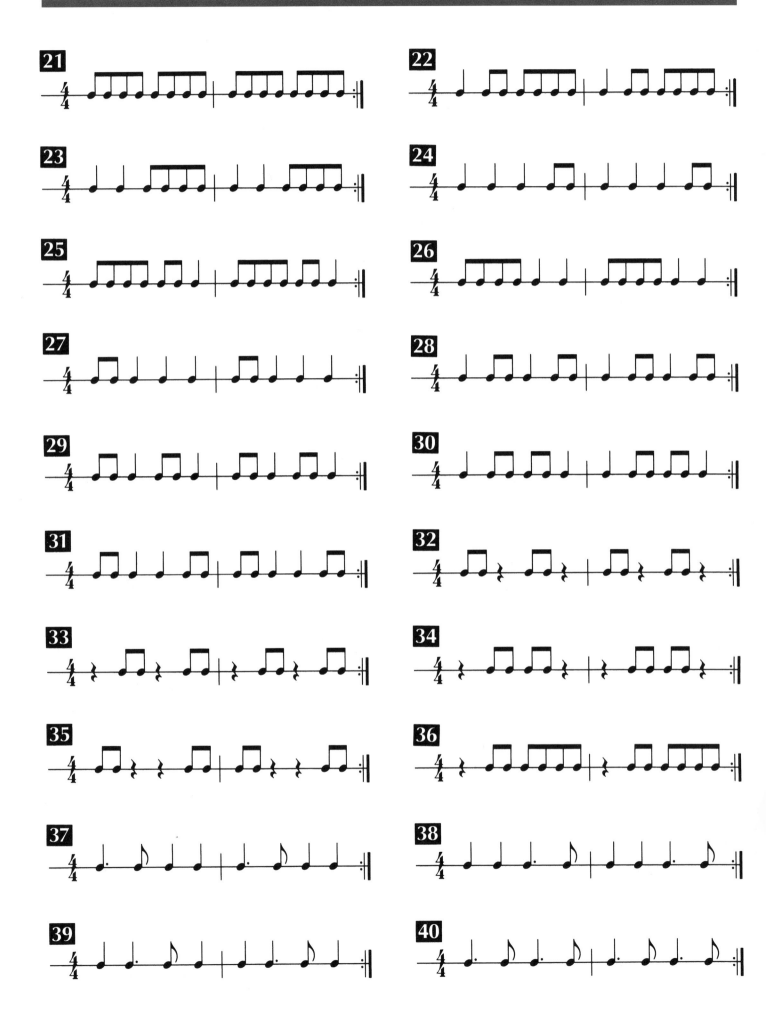

RHYTHM STUDIES

2/4

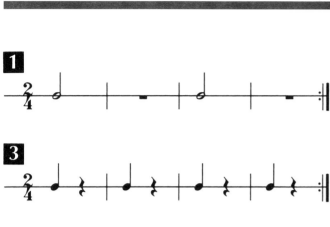

3/4

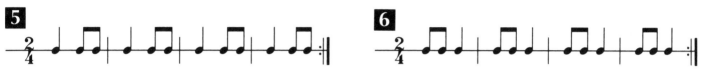

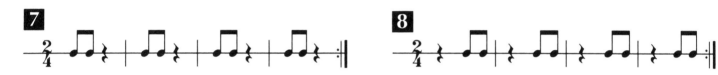

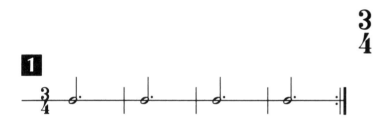

GLOSSARY/INDEX

STANDARD OF EXCELLENCE

EXERCISE 7	notes, rhythm, tone
EXERCISE 12	notes, rhythm, tonguing
EXERCISE 14	notes, rhythm, tone
EXERCISE 17	notes, rhythm, tonguing
EXERCISE 22	notes, rhythm, tone
EXERCISE 23	notes, rhythm, repeat
EXERCISE 29	notes, rhythm, (breath mark)
EXERCISE 31	notes, rhythm, tone
EXERCISE 35	notes, rhythm, hand position
EXERCISE 39	notes, rhythm, breathing
EXERCISE 41	notes, rhythm, repeat
EXERCISE 43	notes, rhythm, hand position
EXERCISE 46	notes, rhythm, tonguing
EXERCISE 49	notes, rhythm, tone
EXERCISE 53	notes, rhythm, tone
EXERCISE 55	notes, rhythm, hand position
EXERCISE 57	notes, rhythm, slurs
EXERCISE 61	notes, rhythm, slurs
EXERCISE 63	notes, rhythm, tone
EXERCISE 67	notes, rhythm, hand position
EXERCISE 70	notes, rhythm, dynamics
EXERCISE 73	notes, rhythm, dynamics
EXERCISE 78	notes, rhythm, tonguing
EXERCISE 79	notes, rhythm, hand position
EXERCISE 82	notes, rhythm, slurs
EXERCISE 84	notes, rhythm, tone
EXERCISE 87	notes, rhythm, accents
EXERCISE 91	notes, rhythm, hand position
EXERCISE 95	notes, rhythm, slurs
EXERCISE 98	notes, rhythm, (repeat sign)
EXERCISE 104	notes, rhythm, dynamics
EXERCISE 106	notes, rhythm, hand position
EXERCISE 111	notes, rhythm, dynamics
EXERCISE 115	notes, rhythm, tone
EXERCISE 117	notes, rhythm, hand position
EXERCISE 122	notes, rhythm, slurs
EXERCISE 126	notes, rhythm, tempo
EXERCISE 128	notes, rhythm, tempo
EXERCISE 131	notes, rhythm, dynamics
EXERCISE 134	notes, rhythm, articulations
EXERCISE 136	notes, rhythm, tonguing
EXERCISE 139	notes, rhythm, repeat
EXERCISE 141	notes, rhythm, tone
EXERCISE 142	notes, rhythm, tempo
EXERCISE 143	notes, rhythm, tempo
EXERCISE 146	notes, rhythm, articulations
EXERCISE 148	notes, rhythm, (breath mark)
EXERCISE 151	notes, rhythm, articulations
EXERCISE 153	notes, rhythm, breathing
EXERCISE 155	notes, rhythm, dynamics

EXCELLENCE

THE FLUTE

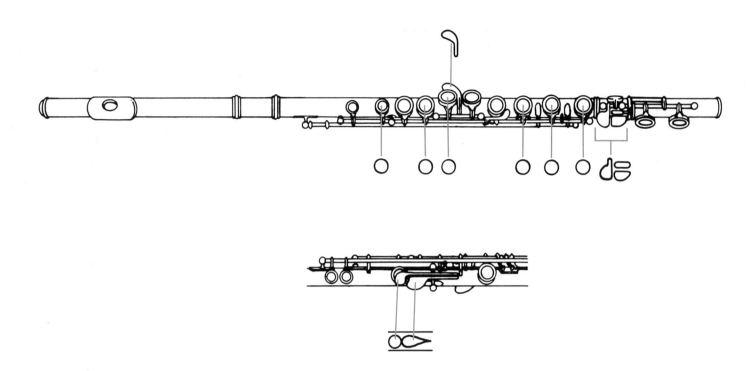

FLUTE HISTORY

The early history of the flute is largely unknown, but most historians agree that it is one of the oldest musical instruments and that it originated somewhere in Central Asia. Members of the early flute family were held either forward or to the side. The first evidence of a transverse flute (held to the side) is found in artwork dating back to 200 B.C. The flute eventually found its way to Germany, where its use became common by the 12th century. Its most popular usage during that time was for military music.

Flutes had only tone holes, without keys, until the late 1600's, when the Baroque flute was invented. It was made of wood, and had seven tone holes and one key for the little finger. It was built in three sections instead of one piece. This helped intonation because the space between the sections could be adjusted. With these improvements, the flute became a regular member of the orchestra and rapidly increased in popularity.

In 1847, Theobald Boehm, a German flautist and goldsmith, completely redesigned the flute. The redesign consisted of two main steps. First, each hole was placed so that each note would have the same tone quality. Second, a key system was added. The Boehm system improved intonation, made the tone of the flute louder, and made notes easier to play. The flute has remained basically unchanged to the present day.

Today, flutes are played in bands, orchestras, woodwind quintets, chamber ensembles, and jazz bands. Flutes are usually made of silver or silver alloy, but can also be made of gold or even platinum. Other types of flutes include the piccolo, alto flute, bass flute, and contrabass flute.

FLUTE SURVIVAL KIT

☐ 2 soft, clean cloths   ☐ key oil
☐ pencil   ☐ method book
☐ band music   ☐ music stand
